Othello

William Shakespeare

Academic Industries, Inc.
West Haven, Connecticut 06516

ISBN 0-88301-767-9

Published by
Academic Industries, Inc.
The Academic Building
Saw Mill Road
West Haven, Connecticut 06516

Printed in the United States of America

about the author

William Shakespeare was born on April 23, 1564, in Stratford-on-Avon, England, the third child of John Shakespeare, a well-to-do merchant, and Mary Arden, his wife. Young William probably attended the Stratford grammar school, where he learned English, Greek, and a great deal of Latin.

In 1582 Shakespeare married Anne Hathaway. By 1583 the couple had a daughter, Susanna, and two years later the twins, Hamnet and Judith. Somewhere between 1585 and 1592 Shakespeare went to London, where he became first an actor and then a playwright. His acting company, The King's Men, appeared most often in the Globe theatre, a part of which Shakespeare himself owned.

In all, Shakespeare is believed to have written thirty-seven plays, several nondramatic poems, and a number of sonnets. In 1611 when he left the active life of the theatre, he returned to Stratford and became a country gentleman, living in the second-largest house in town. For five years he lived a quiet life. Then, on April 23, 1616, William Shakespeare died and was buried in Trinity Church in Stratford. From his own time to the present, Shakespeare is considered one of the greatest writers of the English-speaking world.

William Shakespeare

Othello

Desdemona

Iago

Cassio

Othello

Emilia

Venice is the famous Italian city built along canals bordered with beautiful homes. Many years ago, late at night, two men were walking together.

You are a strange man, Iago! You say you hate Othello, the general you serve so well?

Yes, Roderigo, I do.

Othello had first come as a soldier from another country to serve the people of Venice. Since then he had become a great hero.

Even though I am a better soldier, he chose Michael Cassio to be his next in command!

So now I am only one of his officers instead of a real leader. I hate Othello for this!

Well, I wouldn't continue to serve him if I felt that way.

Oh, but I have a plan, Roderigo. In serving him, I will really be taking care of myself! He will pay dearly for this.

And now the mischief starts! Here is Signior Brabantio's house—let us wake him and let him know that his daughter has been taken away!

Signior Brabantio! Signior Brabantio!

What is the meaning of all this noise . . . and at this hour of the night?

Your daughter, Desdemona, has been stolen away by Othello, the Moor!

What, have you lost your wits? Who are you?

I am Roderigo.

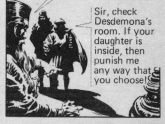

I have told you before that my daughter is not for you! You will be punished for this trick!

Sir, check Desdemona's room. If your daughter is inside, then punish me any way that you choose!

Servants! Bring me a light!

While Brabantio went to look for his daughter, Iago made other plans.

Brabantio was even more upset when he returned.

I must leave now so that Othello doesn't know I've had any part in this.

She is gone! Roderigo, tell me, are they married?

I think so, sir.

Then help me, Roderigo! I will get my soldiers and we will look for them.

Meanwhile, Iago hurried to Othello and told him that his life was in danger.

I wanted to kill Brabantio for the bad things he said about you!

It's good that you didn't, Iago. I love his daughter Desdemona, and I think that he will come to see my side of things.

Just then Cassio arrived with a message.

The duke of Venice is calling for you, General Othello. There is trouble with the Turks in Cyprus. The senate is meeting now.

Here comes Senator Brabantio! Be careful, Othello!

Good Signior Brabantio, this is no time for fighting!

You have taken away my daughter with your magic! I will have you punished!

I will be glad to talk to you about this later. But now I must meet with the duke.

This is true, Signior. I am sure that you have also been sent for.

This late at night? Well, let us go.

Meanwhile, the duke and his advisors were waiting for Othello.

Sir, the reports all say that a fleet of ships from Turkey is headed for Cyprus.

Brave Othello, we beg you to sail for Cyprus right away!

Dear sir, forgive me. I have not come about this business, but about a personal problem. It concerns my daughter!

Why, what is the matter?

Is she dead?

She is as good as dead to me. She has been stolen away by magic!

Whoever has done this will be punished—even if it should be my own son!

I thank you, sir! Here is the man, this Moor!

Othello, what do you have to say?

It is true that I have married this man's daughter—and that I love her.

But I beg you, send for Desdemona and let her tell you whether I used magic to win her love.

Bring Desdemona here!

13

Good Iago, please go for Desdemona. Until she comes, I will tell my part of the story.

Tell us, Othello.

Many times Brabantio, her father, invited me to his house. He always asked me questions about my life and the battles I have fought all over the world.

Desdemona listened as often as she could. Her eyes, as they looked upon me, began to show her love.

I think my very own daughter would have done the same.

Please hear Desdemona speak. Come, child, tell this group about the person you should most obey.

14

My good father, I will always respect you. But now my duty is to my husband, just as my mother's was to you.

That is enough for me. Othello, my daughter is yours. Now let us get on with our problems with Turkey.

Othello, you must sail at once for Cyprus to protect it from the Turks.

I will, sir. But I will need a place for Desdemona to stay.

Oh, yes! I want to go with my husband.

I shall leave it to you, Othello. But you *must* leave tonight.

I will entrust my wife to good Iago. He and his wife Emilia will bring Desdemona to Cyprus.

Goodbye, Othello.

Watch out for her, Moor! If she has deceived her father, she may also deceive *you*!

No, she is faithful to me. Come, Desdemona, we have only a little time left to spend together.

Soon no one was left but Iago and Roderigo.

I suffer too much when I see Desdemona's love for Othello! I think I will drown myself.

Come, be a man! A man would never drown himself for love!

Desdemona will not love the Moor for long. She will be yours, and I will help you get her. Gather all the money you have and bring it to me tomorrow.

I will!

Then Iago was left alone.

What a fool Roderigo is! Yet I can use him and his money in my revenge on Othello. And maybe I can use Cassio to make the Moor crazy with jealousy!

A few days later in Cyprus, some men stood talking.

Good news! The storm that struck us yesterday has sunk most of the enemy ships!

How do you know?

A ship from Venice commanded by Michael Cassio has just landed with the news!

17

It's hard to believe!

Trust me. Cassio will be on guard duty tonight. Make him angry so that he strikes out at you with his sword. If you do, you will be closer to winning Desdemona's love.

When Roderigo had left, Iago continued to plan.

I am sure that Cassio is in love with Desdemona. I think I can make Othello so jealous that he will play right into my hands!

That night the people of Cyprus were invited to a great feast at the castle. They would celebrate the end of the war with Turkey as well as Othello's recent marriage.

Cassio, you are in charge of the guard tonight. Make sure that everything remains peaceful.

But later, when Cassio met Iago, Iago had planned a trap for him.

Welcome, Iago. Let us go to our watch.

It is too early. Let us first have a drink with some of the Cyprus soldiers.

Not tonight, Iago. I get drunk very easily, and I've had one drink already. This is an important night for me to stay sober.

Nonsense! One more drink won't hurt.

Before long, Cassio was drunk.

Do not think, gentlemen, that I have had too much to drink. This is my left hand, and this is my right. And I think I can still walk and can go to my watch.

After Cassio had left them, Iago made matters still worse.

It's too bad Othello puts so much trust in this fellow. He can cause a lot of trouble on this island because of his drinking.

You're right! Someone should warn General Othello about him.

Soon afterward, Iago sent Roderigo after Cassio. As Iago had ordered, Roderigo shouted insults at Cassio. They began to fight, and the soldiers rushed to stop them.

I pray sir, you must stop this! You're drunk! You don't know what you're doing!

Drunk? How can you say I'm drunk?

At this, Cassio started fighting with the soldier. Meanwhile, Iago told Roderigo to run to the town square and sound the alarm. This brought Othello to where the trouble was taking place.

Cassio, never again will you be an officer of mine!

Who started this fight, Iago?

Sir, I do not want to make trouble for Michael Cassio. But it started because he had too much to drink.

When Othello and the others had left, Iago and Cassio remained behind.

You're right, I will ask her tomorrow. Good night, honest Iago.

Don't look so sad, Cassio. Speak to Othello's wife, Desdemona, in the morning. She is very kind and will plead for you before Othello.

The next day, Iago had his wife Emilia arrange a meeting between Desdemona and Cassio.

Now I will fix it so Othello thinks that Desdemona and Cassio are in love.

Cassio, I will try to get my husband to forgive you.

Please don't take too long, or he may forget my service to him. But here he comes—I must not let him see me!

Wasn't that Cassio that just left your wife? He looked guilty and ran when he saw you!

Dear husband, I beg you to forgive Cassio! He truly wants to serve you again!

I don't want to talk about it now, Desdemona.

23

But I shall give you no rest until you change your mind!

I will not deny you anything, Desdemona. But leave us alone for a little while and I will join you soon.

Just as you wish, my dearest. Come Emilia, let us go inside.

But Iago was determined to make Othello jealous. So, when they were alone again, he spoke.

Sir, when you were first courting your lady, did Michael Cassio know of your love?

Oh yes, he went between us often with messages. Why do you ask?

It's nothing, sir. I just can't believe that Cassio would try to trick you.

Iago, as my true friend, are you trying to tell me something about Desdemona and Cassio?

You must be honest with me. Tell me what is on your mind!

Beware of jealousy, dear General.

I will not be jealous without proof. I love and trust my wife.

I am glad to hear it. My advice, then, is this: *Watch Desdemona and Cassio when they are together.*

Remember, Desdemona tricked her father when she married you secretly.

Well, tell Emilia to keep a close watch on her.

Why did I marry? Honest Iago seems to know more than he is telling me!

25

Iago's lies began to work. Left alone, Othello thought of reasons not to trust his wife. When Desdemona came to call him for dinner she found a changed man.

Othello, your dinner and your guests are waiting for you! Are you ill?

I have a headache, that's all.

Let me tie my handkerchief around your head, and it will go away.

No! Your handkerchief is too little. Leave it alone. I'll come with you.

As Othello and Desdemona left, Emilia bent over quickly to pick up the handkerchief that had fallen.

I'm glad I found this. It was Desdemona's first gift from Othello and she loves it. But Iago ordered me to steal it— I have no idea *why*.

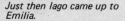
Just then Iago came up to Emilia.

Is this the handkerchief you wanted?

Yes! Give it to me!

This had better be important. Desdemona will be very upset when she learns that it is gone!

I will leave this handkerchief in Cassio's room where he will find it. Othello will go crazy when he sees Cassio with it.

You could not have found a better way to torture me than to make me believe my wife loves another man!

I am sorry to hear this.

You had better show me proof that what you say is true, or you will die!

O world, take note! It does not pay to be an honest man!

I don't know whether to trust you—my good friend, or her—my darling wife. Give me proof of what you say!

For two nights I slept in Cassio's house. Twice I heard him cry out in his sleep, "Sweet Desdemona! Let us hide our love from Othello!"

And there is something more—a handkerchief with strawberries on it.

That was my first gift to Desdemona.

Well, I wouldn't know that. But I saw Michael Cassio wipe his beard with it today!

This proves it! I will get even with them!

Be calm, sir. You may still change your mind.

No! I will have my revenge!

And I will do whatever you ask me.

Dear Iago, trusted friend, within three days I want you to tell me that Cassio is dead. You are now my lieutenant!

I will serve you forever.

29

Later Desdemona and Emilia stood together outside the castle.

Where could I have lost it, Emilia?

I don't know, madam.

I would rather have lost anything but this! But Othello will understand.

Just then Othello drew near.

I hope you will speak to Cassio now!

I have a cold. Please lend me your handkerchief.

Here, dear husband.

That is not the one I mean! Get me the handkerchief I gave you and told you to carry with you always. An Egyptian charmer gave it to my mother.

She told me to give it to my wife. To lose it would mean that terrible things would happen. I hope you have it nearby!

As Othello stormed away, Iago and Cassio came up.

Madam, please keep trying to help me!

He is not himself lately, Cassio. You must wait a little longer.

Is he angry? I will talk with him.

I hope he is worried about business matters and not jealous of you!

I gave him no reason to be!

When Desdemona and Emilia had left, a common lady named Bianca, much in love with Cassio, came forward.

I found this beautiful handkerchief in my room. Would you copy the stitching on it for me?

All right. But won't you walk part way home with me?

Later, when he met Othello again, Iago wanted to make sure that Othello was still very angry.

Suppose Cassio went about bragging that he slept with her?

Has he done that?

If I gave my wife a handkerchief, then it would be hers to give to whomever she likes, wouldn't it?

I would most gladly have forgotten that! But he *did* have my wife's handkerchief.

Oh yes, sir.

Did he? I can't stand this anymore!

And with these words Othello fainted.

At that moment Cassio came up.

What's wrong?

Othello fainted, but I'm taking care of him. Leave us alone for a while, and later I would like to speak with you.

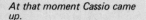

Othello woke in a few moments.

After you fainted, Cassio came by, but I sent him away. If you will hide yourself, I will question him about Desdemona when he returns. You can watch his face even if you can't hear what he says.

All right.

Othello did as Iago said. But worse things were about to happen.

Now I will question Cassio about that woman, Bianca, who loves him so much. Othello will think he is speaking about Desdemona!

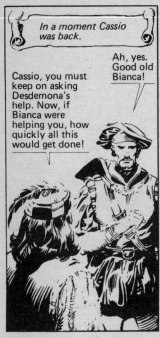

In a moment Cassio was back.

Cassio, you must keep on asking Desdemona's help. Now, if Bianca were helping you, how quickly all this would get done!

Ah, yes. Good old Bianca!

Look how he smiles and laughs in talking about my wife's love for him!

I never saw a woman so in love with a man!

Alas, poor silly woman. She *does* seem to love me!

I will get even with them both!

They say you will soon be marrying her!

She thinks that because it's *her* dream, not mine!

Iago then motioned to Othello to come closer.

She follows me all over the place and hangs about my neck. I can't get rid of her!

Just then Bianca drew near with the handkerchief in her hand.

I am not going to spend my time copying the work that some other woman has given you!

Why, that is the handkerchief I gave Desdemona!

35

But I only say what she is. She sews so well, and her voice is beautiful. Why, she could sing the wildness out of a bear!

That only makes it worse!

Get me some poison, Iago. I will kill her this very night!

No, do not use poison. Strangle her in her bed!

And let me take care of Cassio. You shall hear more about this by midnight.

Very good!

Just then a trumpet sounded.

What is this?

It must mean a visitor from Venice.

At that moment, Lodovico, one of Desdemona's relatives from Venice, came forward.

Greetings, good general! The duke sends you this letter.

And what's the news, good cousin Lodovico?

I am glad to see you, sir. Welcome to Cyprus.

I thank you. How is Lieutenant Cassio?

He is alive.

There has been a problem between him and my husband. But I am sure that you will make all things well again.

Are you so sure of that?

Pardon me?

So—there is a problem between Othello and Cassio?

A most unhappy one. I would do much to make them friends again, for the love I feel toward Cassio!

What?

Is he angry?

It may be the letter. He has just been ordered back to Venice, and Cassio has been put in command here in Cyprus.

Oh, I'm glad!

And at that, before all the company, Othello struck Desdemona in the face.

I have not deserved this!

Sir! This would not be believed in Venice! Beg her pardon! She weeps!

They are crocodile tears. Get out of my sight, woman! I'll send for you later.

Sir, I obey the order. I will return to Venice and leave Cassio here in my place. Now please excuse me.

Lodovico was shocked to see Othello strike Desdemona. He spoke to Iago.

Is this the noble Moor our senate admires so?

He is much changed. I only hope this is the *worst* he does!

Later, Othello questioned Emilia about Desdemona.

Have you noticed Desdemona and Cassio trying to be alone? Have they sent you away on some small excuse?

Of course not! She is the most honest, faithful woman I know. If anyone has put this thought into your head, a snake should strike him!

All right. Go now, and bring Desdemona here.

I don't believe Emilia either.

And when Desdemona came before him, Othello was still in an angry mood.

Let me look into your eyes.

I can see your anger, sir, but I do not understand your words. I am your loyal wife.

Are you not an unfaithful wife who has fallen in love with another man?

Never! My only wish has been to serve and please you!

But Othello's jealousy had gone too far. Desdemona could no longer reach him with her simple words.

Good lady, what is the matter with your husband?

I no longer have the husband I once had. Please call Iago, Emilia. I would like to talk with him.

But when Iago came, Desdemona was weeping.

What is the matter, lady?

Alas, Iago. Othello has told her that she is untrue to him. He is very angry.

Have I been untrue in any way, Iago?

Do not weep, do not weep! Of course not!

Desdemona had the chance to marry many noble men. She gave them all up to marry Othello! And now he calls her unfaithful!

How did this happen?

Perhaps some evil person—in order to gain some high rank—has done this awful thing!

O good Iago, what shall I do to win him back again? Please go to him for me!

43

I am sure that his bad mood comes from some business matter. Ah, I hear the trumpets calling you to supper. Go and eat. I will make everything well again!

When Desdemona and Emilia had left, Iago met Roderigo.

Iago, I do not think you are being fair. You haven't spoken of me to Desdemona as you promised. I am going to see her myself.

You have taken all my jewels as well as my money. You said you gave the jewels to Desdemona, but I have had no word from her. I want my jewels back!

Well, Roderigo, you do have some nerve after all! I think the better of you for it.

But I *have* been working for you!

Not that *I* can see!

Well, you must do one more thing before Desdemona is all yours. It will take courage!

Othello has been ordered to Mauritania and Cassio will take his place here. Othello will bring Desdemona with him if he goes. To keep them here, Cassio must have an accident.

What do you mean?

Cassio must be killed —otherwise Desdemona will be lost to you. And just as you were about to win her!

45

Meanwhile, dinner had been finished, and people were leaving the hall.

Madam, good night. I humbly thank you.

You are most welcome.

Gentlemen, I will walk a little way with you. Desdemona, go right to bed. I will be up a little later. Send Emilia away!

Later, in the bedroom, Desdemona spoke with Emilia.

Help me with my things, Emilia, and then leave. Othello has ordered it, and we must not displease him.

I wish you had never seen him!

Ah, but I still love him. Good night, Emilia, good night.

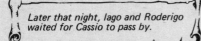

Later that night, Iago and Roderigo waited for Cassio to pass by.

I've made Roderigo mad enough to kill Cassio. But whether he kills Cassio or Cassio kills him—or they kill each other, I will gain.

Stand behind this wall and keep your sword ready. Fear nothing, and be quick!

Stay near me in case I miss him.

If Cassio lives, he will find out about me and tell Othello. He *must* die!

Here he comes! Die, Cassio!

That missed me, but I've hurt him instead.

Cassio wounded Roderigo. But from behind, Iago drove his sword into Cassio's leg.

Now I am hurt! Help! Murder!

Just then Othello came by on his way back to the castle.

That is Cassio calling for help. Iago has kept his word. Now I must keep *my* promise to kill Desdemona.

Soon after this, Desdemona's cousin Lodovico and another relative named Gratiano came by. They had been drawn to the same spot by the cries of Cassio and Roderigo. Iago came forth as though he had just arrived.

Who cries murder?

We don't know!

Iago, please help me! I have been stabbed. One of the men who did it is nearby and is also hurt.

Help me, here!

That's one of them!

Quickly, and without being seen, Iago stabbed Roderigo, and Roderigo grew still.

Just then Bianca came by and found Cassio.

Who are these people who kill men in the dark? Murder! Murder! Wake the townspeople!

Who calls murder? Oh, my dear Cassio!

Cassio, do you know who tried to kill you? This woman may have been one of them!

Cassio must be carried away to be taken care of. But—good heavens! The other man is Roderigo!

I know him from Venice!

Men, carry him carefully! Cassio, do you know why Roderigo wanted to kill you?

Not at all. I don't even *know* him.

Gentlemen, look how pale this woman is. Her guilt shows in her face.

Just then Emilia came by.

What is the matter here, Iago?

Cassio was attacked in the dark by Roderigo. Cassio is hurt, and Roderigo is dead!

Was Cassio at your house earlier? Answer, woman!

Cassio was at my house, but I am an honest woman. I have done nothing wrong.

Emilia, run to the castle and tell Othello what has happened!

This is the night that either solves my problems or kills me for trying!

While all this was taking place outside the castle, Othello had returned to his bedroom and found Desdemona asleep.

You are the cause of it all! But I will not shed your blood, for you are too beautiful for that. Still . . . you must die.

I weep for you, but they are tears that have brought me too much suffering. Ah, she's waking up.

Who's there? Othello!

Have you prayed tonight, Desdemona?

51

Yes, dear husband.

If you want to ask God's pardon for anything, do it now. I would not want to kill your soul!

Are you going to kill me? My only sin is that of loving you too much.

What about the handkerchief I gave you? You gave it to Cassio!

I did not! Send for the man and ask him!

But I saw the handkerchief in his hand. He also bragged that you loved him!

Send for him!

He is dead! Iago has taken care of that.

Oh, husband! Let me live tonight . . . kill me tomorrow! Or at least give me more time to pray!

No, this is the end. I dare not wait any longer.

As Othello smothered Desdemona, Emilia's voice was heard outside the door.

Sir! General Othello!

What noise is that?

Sir, I must speak a word with you!

That is Emilia. She's come to tell me of Cassio's death.

53

If she comes in she'll see that my wife is dead! My wife—what wife? I no longer have a wife!

Sir, I beg you, I must speak with you!

I will pull the curtains and open the door.

Come in, Emilia. What's the matter?

Sir, Cassio has killed a young man of Venice called Roderigo.

And Cassio is killed?

No, Cassio is not killed.

Oh, wrongly, wrongly murdered!

Whose cry is that?

That was Desdemona's voice! Sweet Desdemona, speak! Who did this to you?

I, myself. Farewell.

No—I killed her!

Then she is an angel and you are a devil!

She was false!

She was true!

Your husband proved to me that she was false. He knew it all!

My husband?

55

If my husband said that, may his soul rot forever! You may kill me too, but I will speak the truth. Help! Help! Othello has murdered his wife!

At that, people rushed into the room.

What is the matter?

Iago, you have done it now. These murders all lead back to your planning!

Prove that you are honest if you can! Othello said you told him that his wife was false!

Did you tell him that?

I only told him what I thought. Now be quiet!

I will speak! Desdemona lies here—murdered in her bed because of your lies!

You have killed the most innocent woman who ever lived!

She was false to me! She gave Cassio the handkerchief I gave her. It was a very special thing to us.

Oh, *no*!

If it costs me my life, I will tell the truth!

Iago begged me to steal the handkerchief, but I found it and gave it to him.

You lie!

With that, Iago plunged his sword into Emilia and ran out of the room.

Someone stand at the door and guard Othello while we go after Iago!

Oh Desdemona, Desdemona!

The men soon came back with Iago.

I know you are a devil, so I can only *hurt* you—I can't *kill* you.

Take Othello's sword.

At this, Cassio drew near as Lodovico questioned Othello.

Did you and Iago plan to kill Cassio?

Yes, we did.

Dear Othello, I never gave you reason to hate me so!

I do believe it now. But why did Iago do this to me?

What you know, you know. I will never speak again.

We will make him talk.

Wait! The letters found in Roderigo's pocket show how Iago used him to stir up trouble for Cassio. They say also that Iago took Roderigo's money and jewels, pretending to give them to Desdemona.

Cassio, how did you get my wife's handkerchief?

I found it in my room. Iago confessed that he put it there.

59

Now you must come with us, Othello. Cassio will be in charge here in Cyprus.

I have loyally served the state of Venice. When you tell them what I have done, please speak of me as one that loved not wisely, but too well.

Once, in another land, I protected a man of Venice from a Turk who had attacked him. I killed the Turk—like this!

Then Othello pulled a hidden knife from his shirt and stabbed himself.

COMPLETE LIST OF POCKET CLASSICS AVAILABLE

CLASSICS

C 1 Black Beauty
C 2 The Call of the Wild
C 3 Dr. Jekyll and Mr. Hyde
C 4 Dracula
C 5 Frankenstein
C 6 Huckleberry Finn
C 7 Moby Dick
C 8 The Red Badge of Courage
C 9 The Time Machine
C10 Tom Sawyer
C11 Treasure Island
C12 20,000 Leagues Under the Sea
C13 The Great Adventures of Sherlock Holmes
C14 Gulliver's Travels
C15 The Hunchback of Notre Dame
C16 The Invisible Man
C17 Journey to the Center of the Earth
C18 Kidnapped
C19 The Mysterious Island
C20 The Scarlet Letter
C21 The Story of My Life
C22 A Tale of Two Cities
C23 The Three Musketeers
C24 The War of the Worlds
C25 Around the World in Eighty Days
C26 Captains Courageous
C27 A Connecticut Yankee in King Arthur's Court
C28 The Hound of the Baskervilles
C29 The House of the Seven Gables
C30 Jane Eyre
C31 The Last of the Mohicans
C32 The Best of O. Henry
C33 The Best of Poe
C34 Two Years Before the Mast
C35 White Fang
C36 Wuthering Heights
C37 Ben Hur
C38 A Christmas Carol
C39 The Food of the Gods
C40 Ivanhoe
C41 The Man in the Iron Mask
C42 The Prince and the Pauper
C43 The Prisoner of Zenda
C44 The Return of the Native
C45 Robinson Crusoe
C46 The Scarlet Pimpernel

C47 The Sea Wolf
C48 The Swiss Family Robinson
C49 Billy Budd
C50 Crime and Punishment
C51 Don Quixote
C52 Great Expectations
C53 Heidi
C54 The Illiad
C55 Lord Jim
C56 The Mutiny on Board H.M.S. Bounty
C57 The Odyssey
C58 Oliver Twist
C59 Pride and Prejudice
C60 The Turn of the Screw

SHAKESPEARE

S 1 As You Like It
S 2 Hamlet
S 3 Julius Caesar
S 4 King Lear
S 5 Macbeth
S 6 The Merchant of Venice
S 7 A Midsummer Night's Dream
S 8 Othello
S 9 Romeo and Juliet
S10 The Taming of the Shrew
S11 The Tempest
S12 Twelfth Night